Pyotr Ilyich TCHAIKOVSKY

FRANCESCA DA RIMINI

Op. 32

Edited by
Clark McAlister

Study Score
Partitur

SERENISSIMA MUSIC, INC.

Perviene Dante nel secondo cerchio dello inferno. Quivi vede, che sono puniti i lussuriosi, la pena dei quali è l'essere tormentati di continuo da crudelissimi venti sotto oscuro e tenebroso aere. Fra questi tormentati riconosce Francesca da Rimini che racconta la sua storia.

> . . . "Nessun maggior dolore
> che ricordarsi del tempo felice
> ne la miseria; e ciò sa 'l tuo dottore.
>   Ma s'a conoscer la prima radice
> del nostro amor tu hai cotanto affetto, dirò
> come colui che piange e dice.
>   Noi leggiavamo un giorno per diletto di
> Lancialotto come amor lo strinse;
> soli eravamo e sanza alcun sospetto.
>   Per più fiate li occhi ci sospinse
> quella lettura, e scolorocci il viso;
> ma solo un punto fu quel che ci vinse.
>   Quando leggemmo il disïato riso
> esser basciato da cotanto amante, questi,
> che mai da me non fia diviso,
>   la bocca mi basciò tutto tremante.
> Galeotto fu 'l libro e chi lo scrisse:
> quel giorno più non vi leggemmo avante."
>   Mentre che l'uno spirto questo disse,
> l'altro piangëa sì che di pietade
> io venni men così com' io morisse,
>   e caddi come corpo morto cade.

Dante, **Inferno**, Canto V, ll. 121---142

Dante descends to the second circle of Hell. There he sees those being punished for sins of lust, the punishment for which is to be continuously tormented by the cruelest winds which blow constantly in total darkness. Among those in torment he recognizes Francesca da Rimini, who tells her story:

"There is no greater sorrow than remembering a happy time when one is in misery, as your teacher knows. But if you want to know the first root of our love, I will tell you [about it] although to do so will be like weeping when I speak. One day we were reading for pleasure of Lancelot and how he was overwhelmed by love; we were alone and above suspicion. Several times our eyes met because of what we were reading, and our faces went pale; but at one point we were overcome. When we read how the smile so much desired was kissed by such a lover, he who will never be separated from me kissed my trembling mouth. Guilty was the book and its writer, Galeotto, and that day we read no further."

While one spirit told this story, the other wept so piteously that I fainted out of compassion, and I fell as though dead.

ORCHESTRA

3 Flutes (3rd also Piccolo)

2 Oboes

English horn

2 Clarinets in C

2 Bassoons

4 Horns in F

2 Cornets in B-flat

2 Trumpets in B-flat

3 Trombones

Tuba

Timpani

Percussion
(Bass Drum, Cymbals, Tam-Tam)

Harp

Violin I

Violin II

Viola

Violoncello

Bass

Duration: ca.25 minutes

First performance: March 9, 1877
Russian Musical Society Concert
RMS Orchestra, Nikolay Rubinstein (conductor)

© Copyright 2012 Clark McAlister
All rights reserved.

The large score and a complete set of parts are available for sale from
Serenissima Music, Inc. Previously issued by E.F. Kalmus as A2168
under the pseudonym Howard K. Wolf.

FRANCESCA DA RIMINI
Symphonic Fantasia after Dante

PYOTR ILYICH TCHAIKOVSKY, Op.32
Performing Edition by Clark McAlister

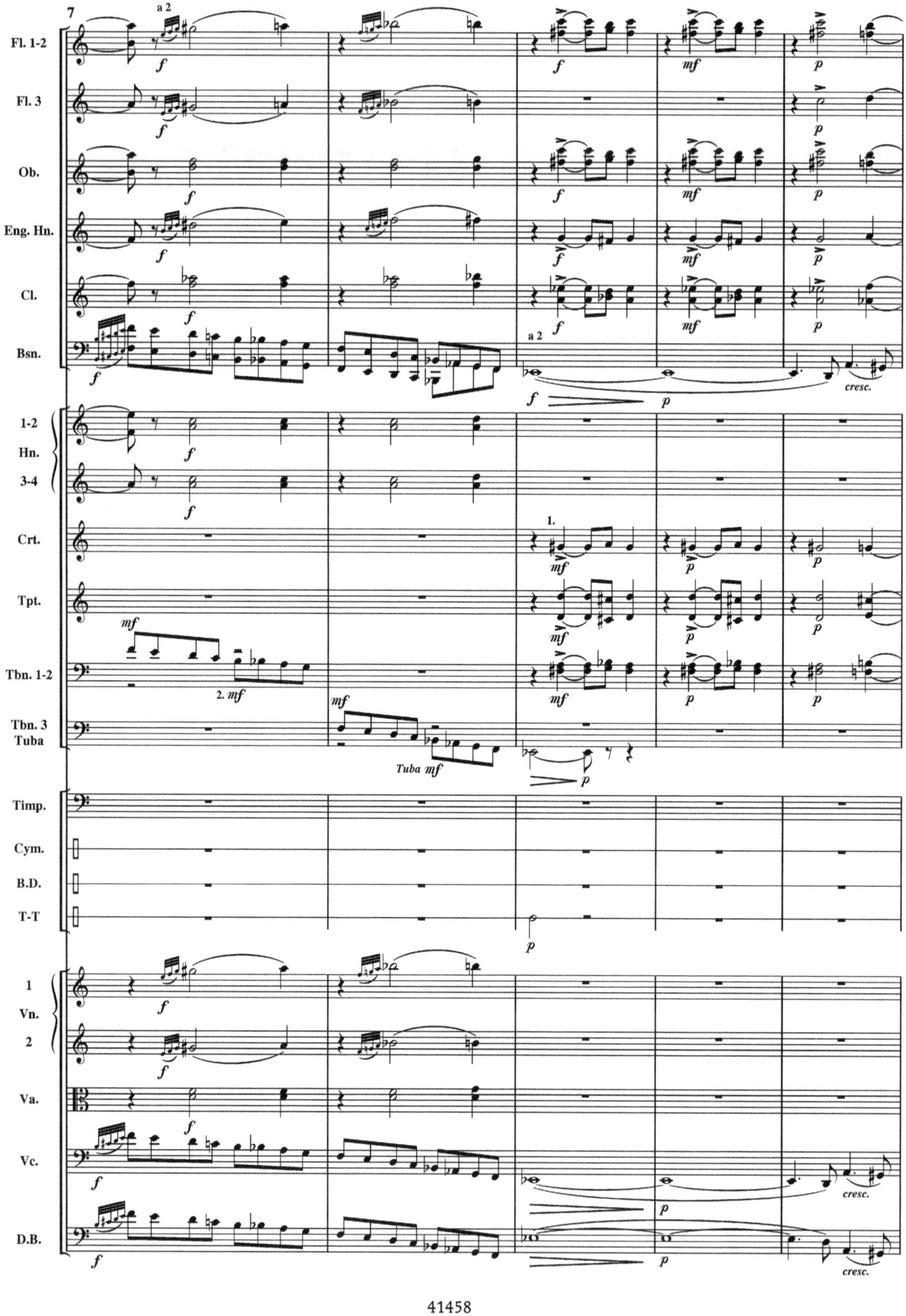
7
Fl. 1-2
Fl. 3
Ob.
Eng. Hn.
Cl.
Bsn.
1-2
Hn.
3-4
Crt.
Tpt.
Tbn. 1-2
Tbn. 3
Tuba
Timp.
Cym.
B.D.
T-T
1
Vn.
2
Va.
Vc.
D.B.
a 2
1.
2. mf
Tuba mf
cresc.

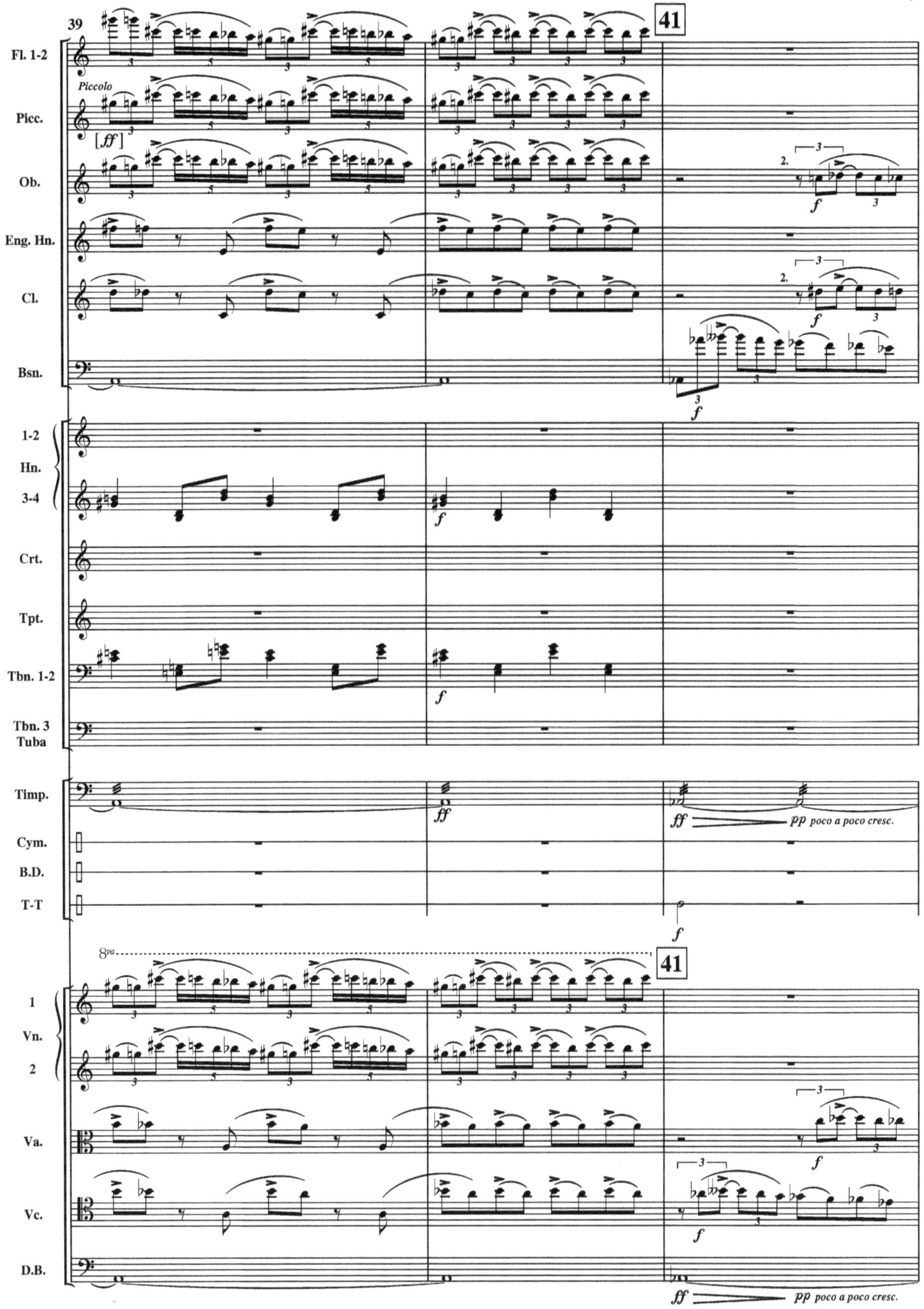
39
41
Fl. 1-2
Piccolo
Picc.
[ff]
Ob.
2.
f
Eng. Hn.
Cl.
Bsn.
1-2
Hn.
3-4
Crt.
Tpt.
Tbn. 1-2
Tbn. 3
Tuba
Timp.
ff
pp poco a poco cresc.
Cym.
B.D.
T-T
8va
1
Vn.
2
Va.
Vc.
D.B.

14

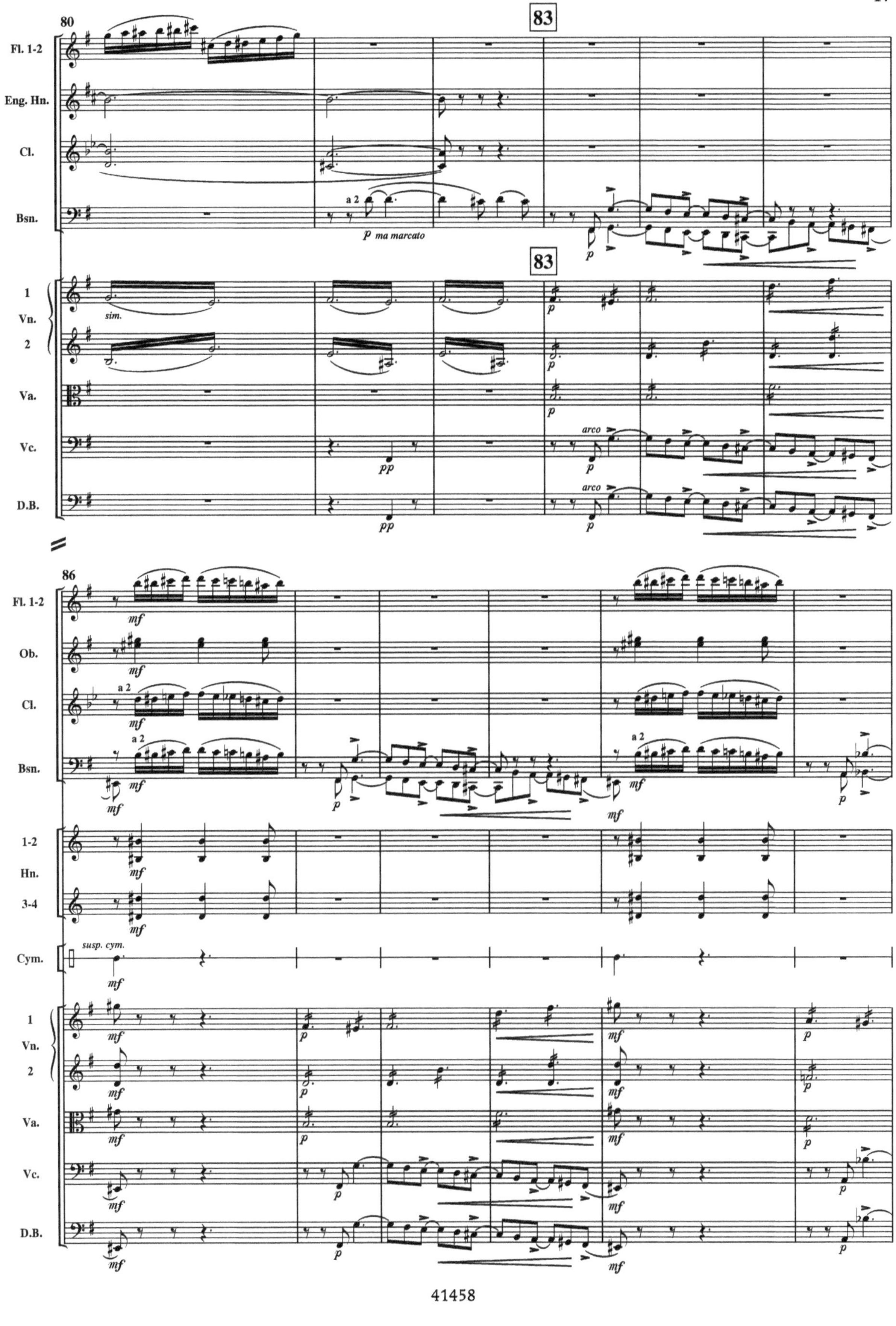
80
83
Fl. 1-2
Eng. Hn.
Cl.
Bsn.
a 2
p ma marcato
Vn.
sim.
Va.
Vc.
arco
pp
D.B.
86
Ob.
Hn.
1-2
3-4
Cym.
susp. cym.
mf
p

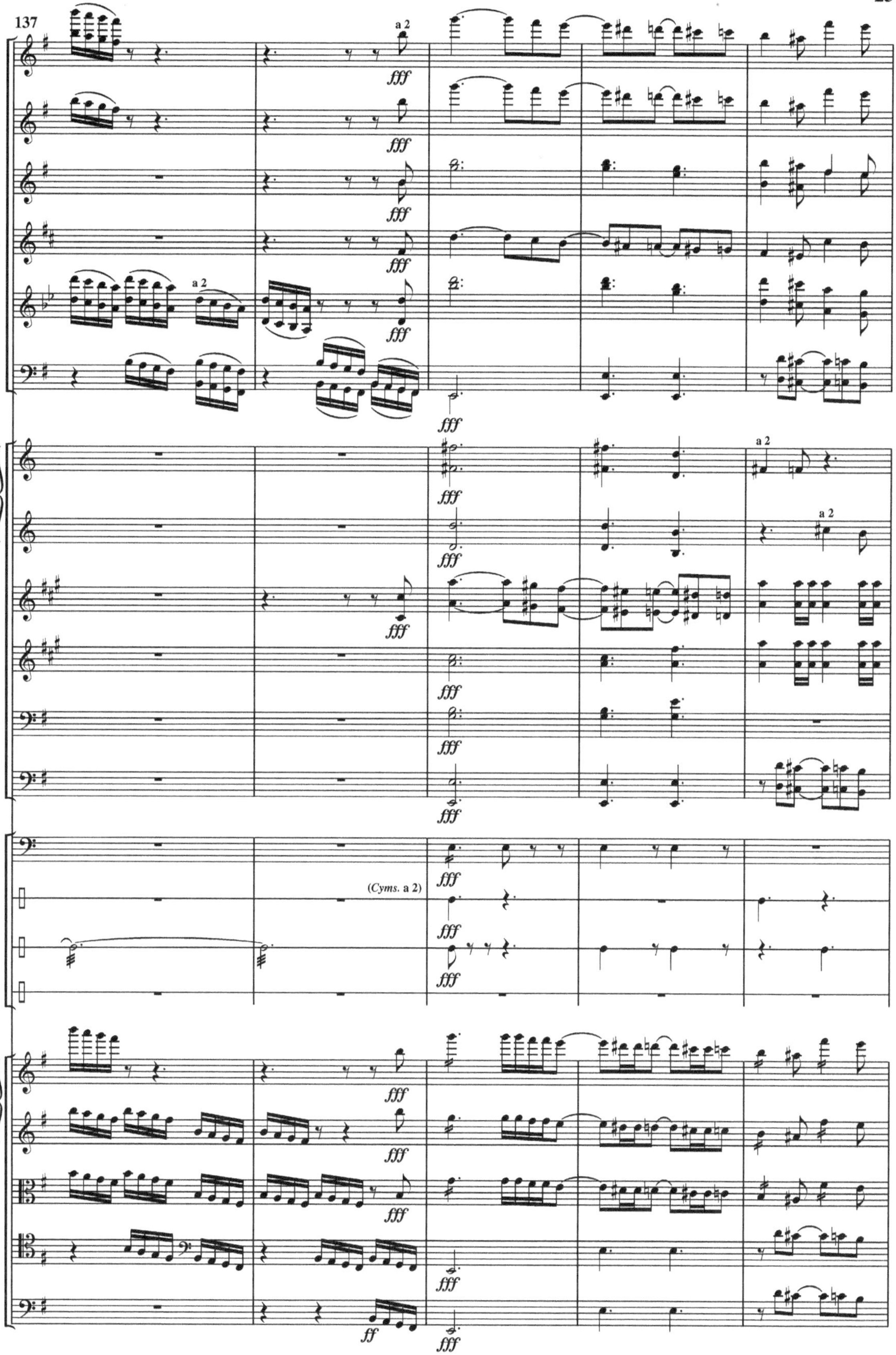
137
Fl. 1-2
Picc.
Ob.
Eng. Hn.
Cl.
Bsn.
1-2
Hn.
3-4
Crt.
Tpt.
Tbn. 1-2
Tbn. 3
Tuba
Timp.
Cym.
B.D.
T-T
1
Vn.
2
Va.
Vc.
D.B.
a 2
fff
ff
(Cyms. a 2)

26

33

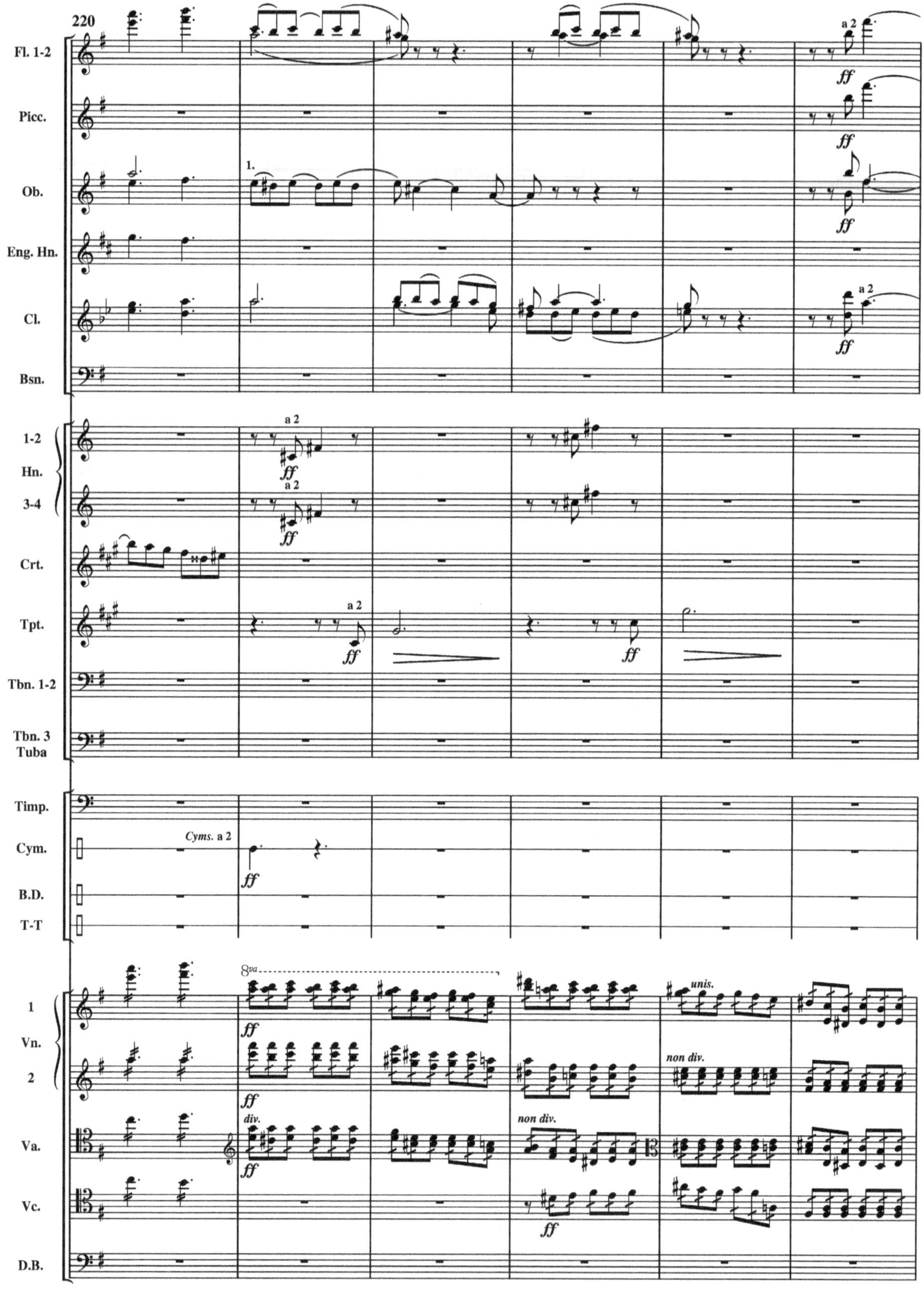
220
Fl. 1-2
Picc.
Ob.
Eng. Hn.
Cl.
Bsn.
1-2
Hn.
3-4
Crt.
Tpt.
Tbn. 1-2
Tbn. 3
Tuba
Timp.
Cym.
B.D.
T-T
1
Vn.
2
Va.
Vc.
D.B.
a 2
ff
1.
Cyms. a 2
8va
div.
non div.
unis.

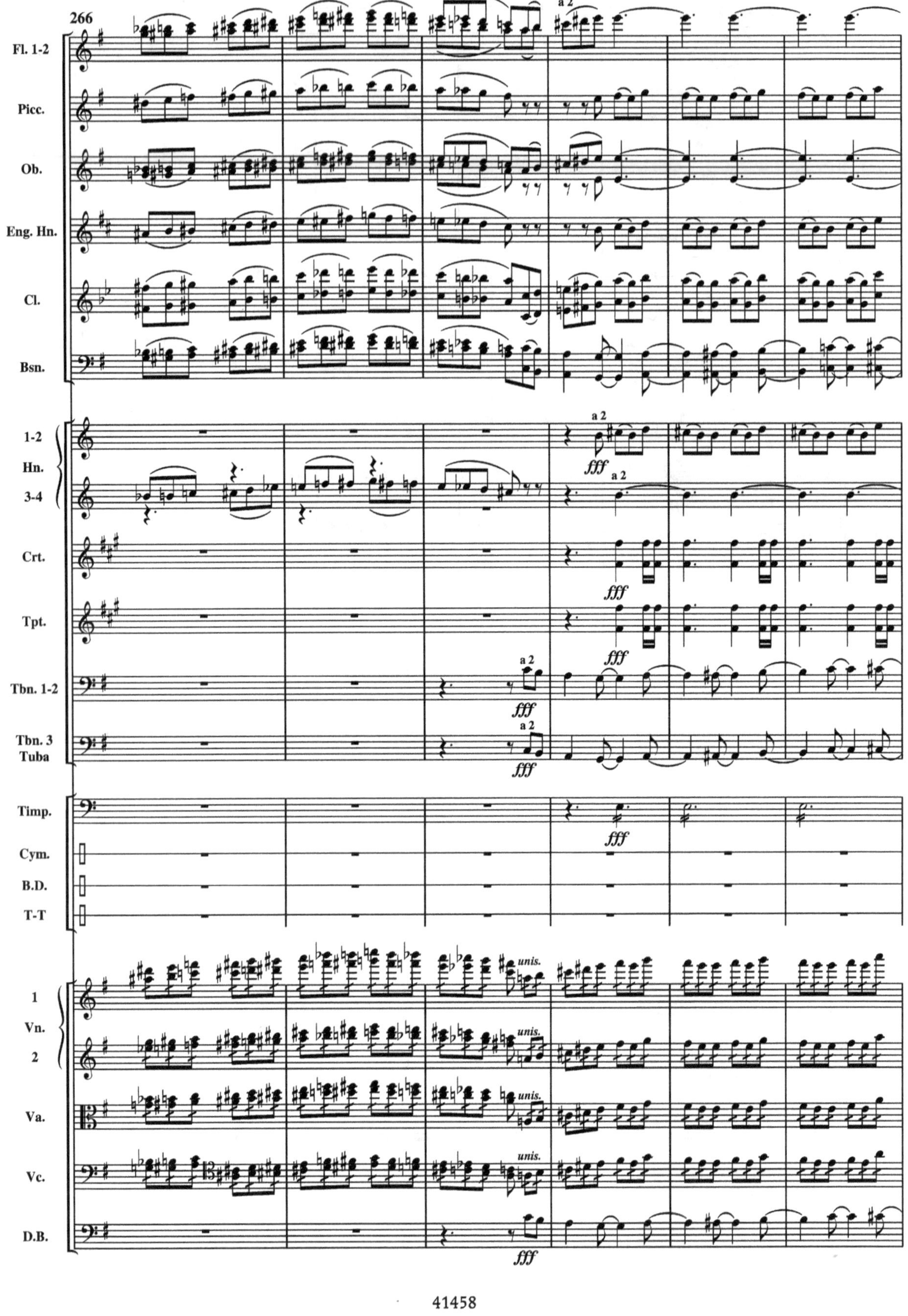
266
Fl. 1-2
a 2
Picc.
Ob.
Eng. Hn.
Cl.
Bsn.
1-2
Hn.
3-4
a 2
fff
a 2
Crt.
fff
Tpt.
fff
Tbn. 1-2
a 2
fff
Tbn. 3
Tuba
a 2
fff
Timp.
fff
Cym.
B.D.
T-T
1
Vn.
2
unis.
unis.
Va.
unis.
Vc.
unis.
D.B.
fff

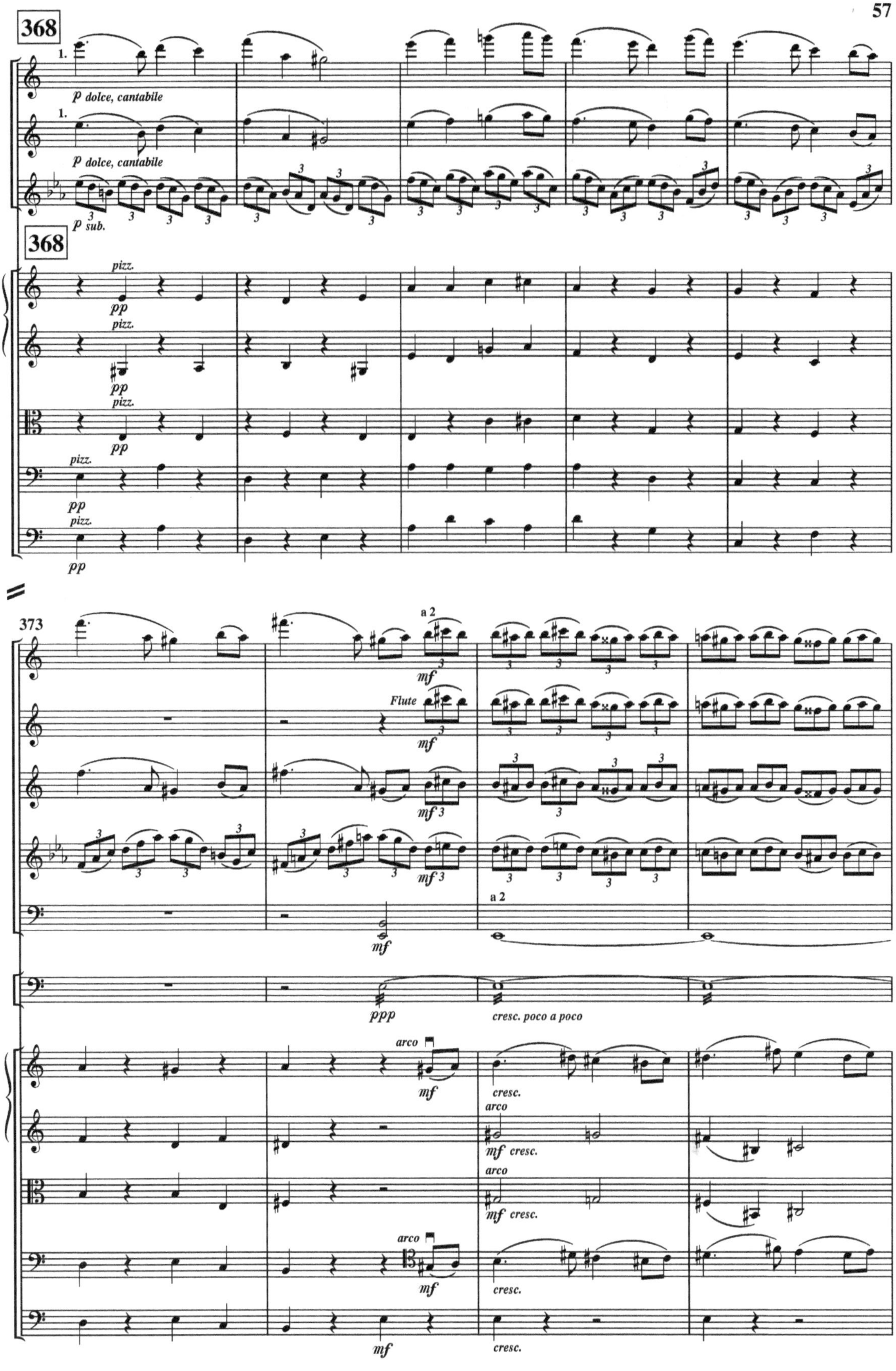
368
1.
Fl. 1-2
p dolce, cantabile
1.
Ob.
p dolce, cantabile
Cl.
p sub.
368
1
Vn.
2
pizz.
pp
pizz.
pp
Va.
pizz.
pp
Vc.
pizz.
pp
D.B.
pizz.
pp
373
Fl. 1-2
a 2
mf
Fl. 3
Flute
mf
Ob.
mf
Cl.
mf
Bsn.
mf
a 2
Timp.
ppp
cresc. poco a poco
1
Vn.
2
arco
mf
cresc.
arco
mf cresc.
Va.
arco
mf cresc.
Vc.
arco
mf
cresc.
D.B.
mf
cresc.

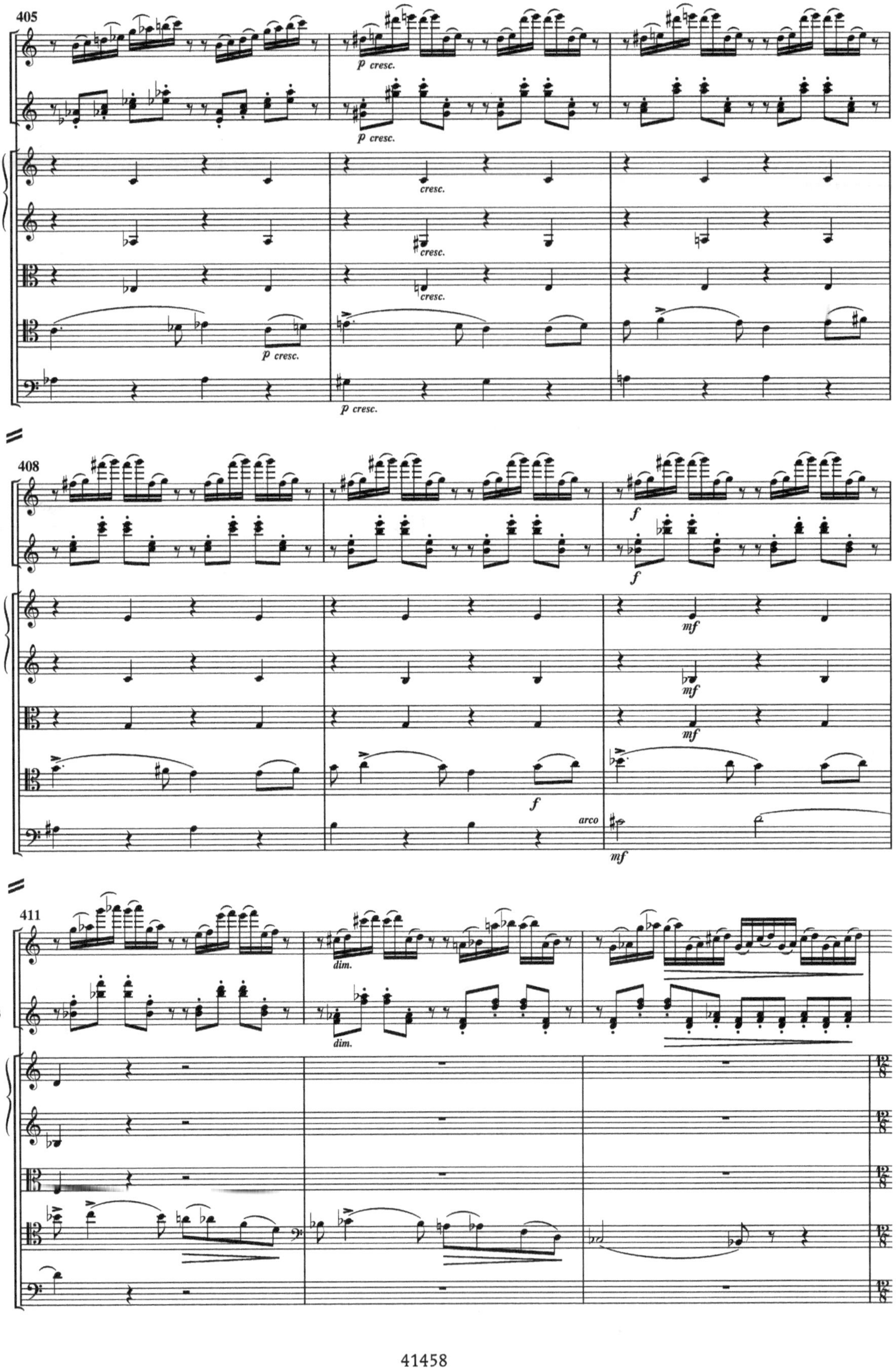
405
Fl. 1
Fl. 2-3
1
Vn.
2
Va.
Vc.
D.B.
p cresc.
p cresc.
cresc.
cresc.
cresc.
p cresc.
p cresc.
408
f
f
mf
mf
mf
f
arco
mf
411
dim.
dim.

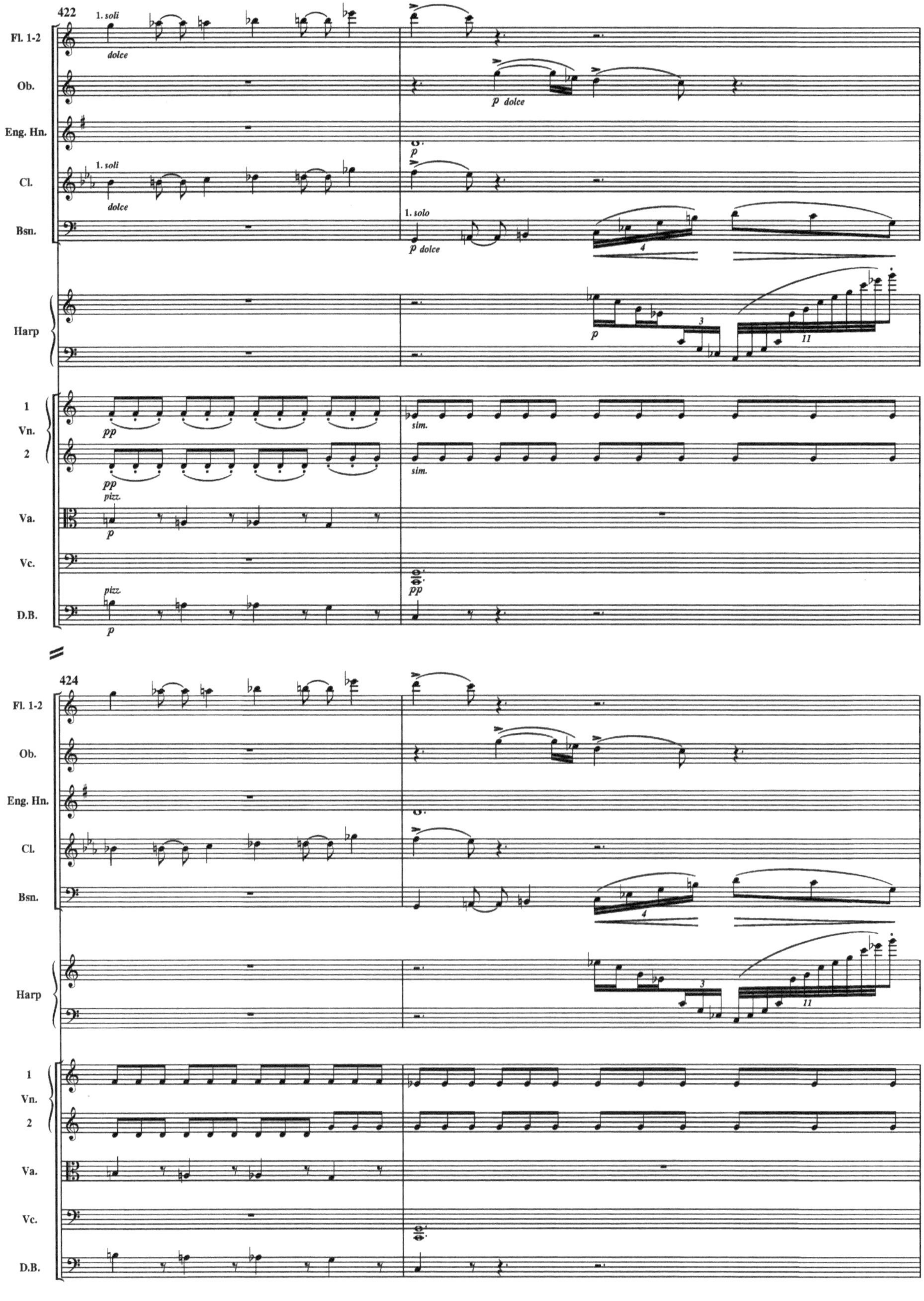
422
Fl. 1-2
Ob.
Eng. Hn.
Cl.
Bsn.
Harp
1
Vn.
2
Va.
Vc.
D.B.
1. soli
dolce
p dolce
p
1. soli
dolce
1. solo
p dolce
4
p
3
11
pp
sim.
pp
sim.
pizz.
p
pp
pizz.
p
424
Fl. 1-2
Ob.
Eng. Hn.
Cl.
Bsn.
Harp
1
Vn.
2
Va.
Vc.
D.B.
4
3
11

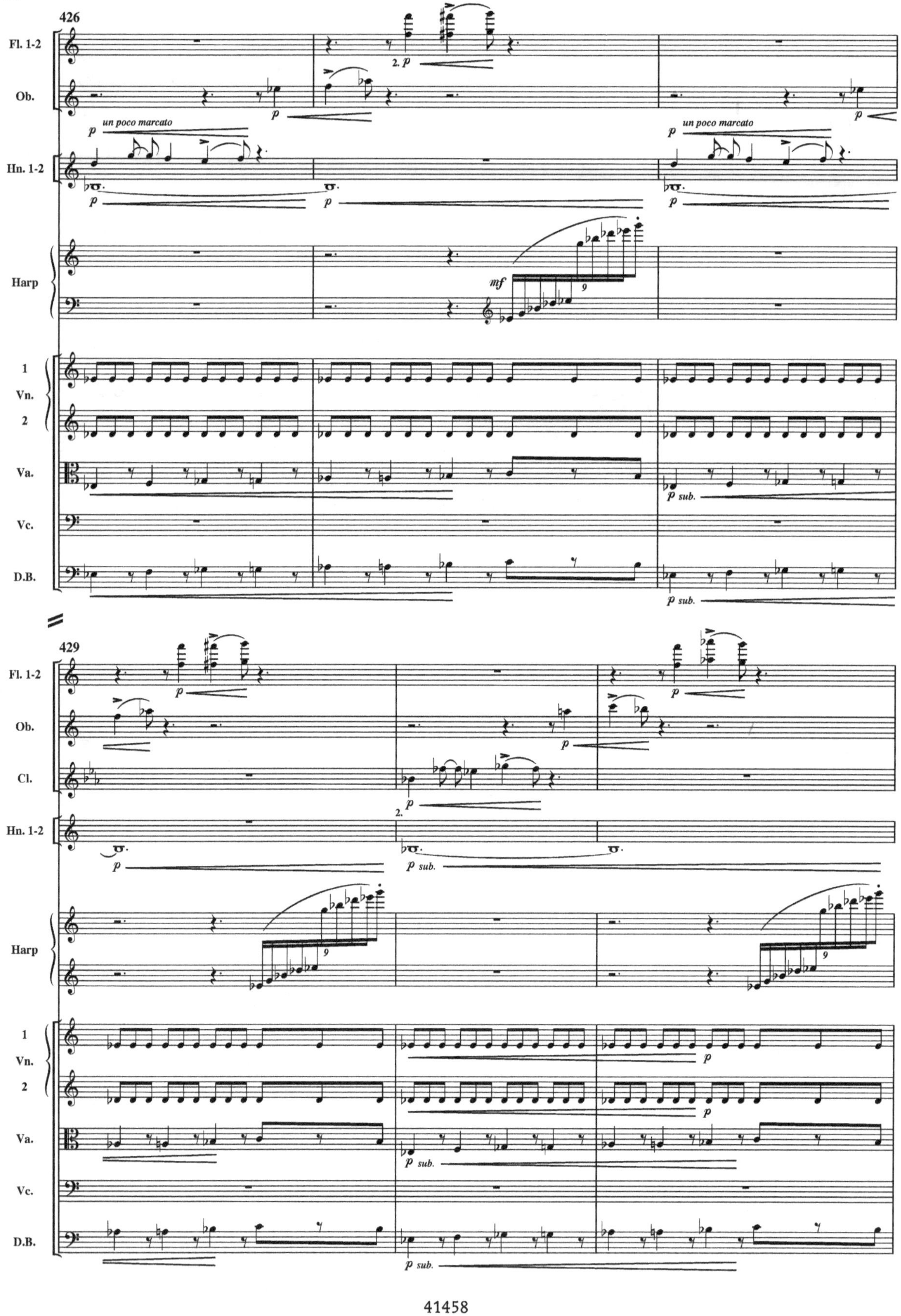
426
Fl. 1-2
Ob.
Hn. 1-2
Harp
Vn.
Va.
Vc.
D.B.
un poco marcato
2.
p sub.
429
Cl.
mf
9

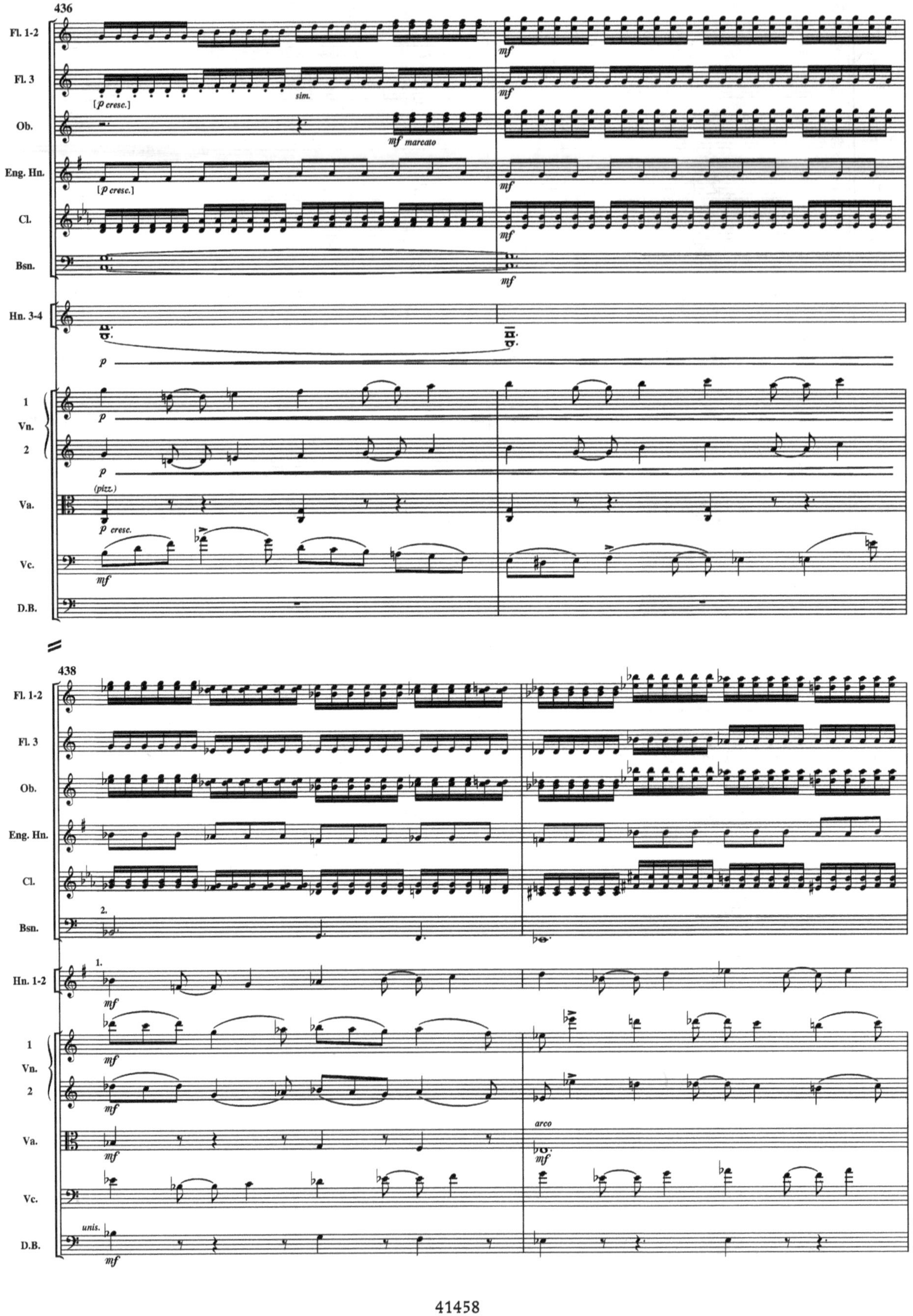
436
Fl. 1-2
Fl. 3
[p cresc.]
sim.
Ob.
mf marcato
Eng. Hn.
[p cresc.]
Cl.
Bsn.
mf
Hn. 3-4
p
1
Vn.
2
Va.
(pizz.)
p cresc.
Vc.
D.B.
438
Fl. 1-2
Fl. 3
Ob.
Eng. Hn.
Cl.
Bsn.
2.
Hn. 1-2
1.
mf
Va.
arco
Vc.
D.B.
unis.

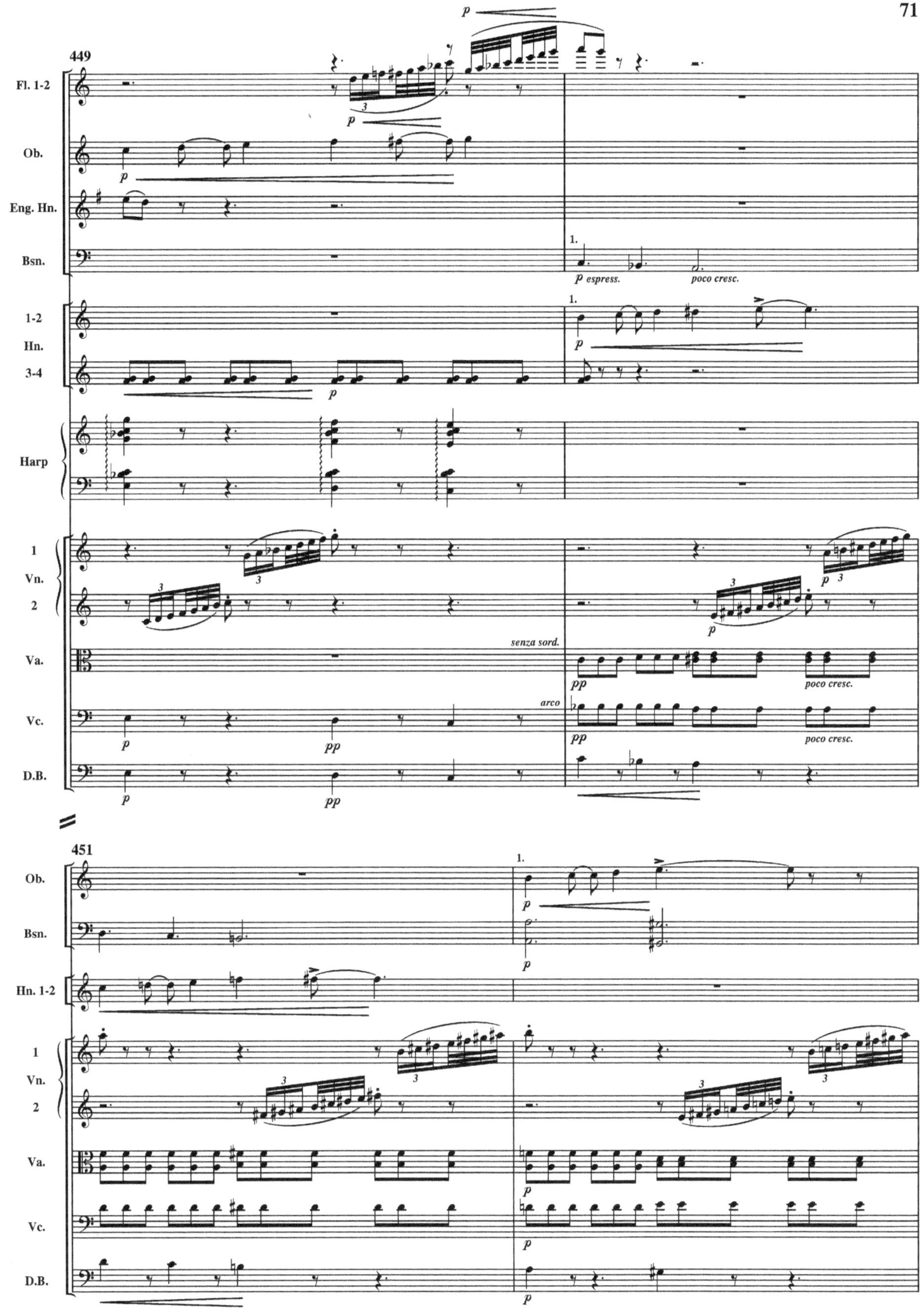
449
Fl. 1-2
Ob.
Eng. Hn.
Bsn.
1-2
Hn.
3-4
Harp
1
Vn.
2
Va.
Vc.
D.B.
espress.
poco cresc.
senza sord.
arco
poco cresc.
poco cresc.
451
Ob.
Bsn.
Hn. 1-2
1
Vn.
2
Va.
Vc.
D.B.

72

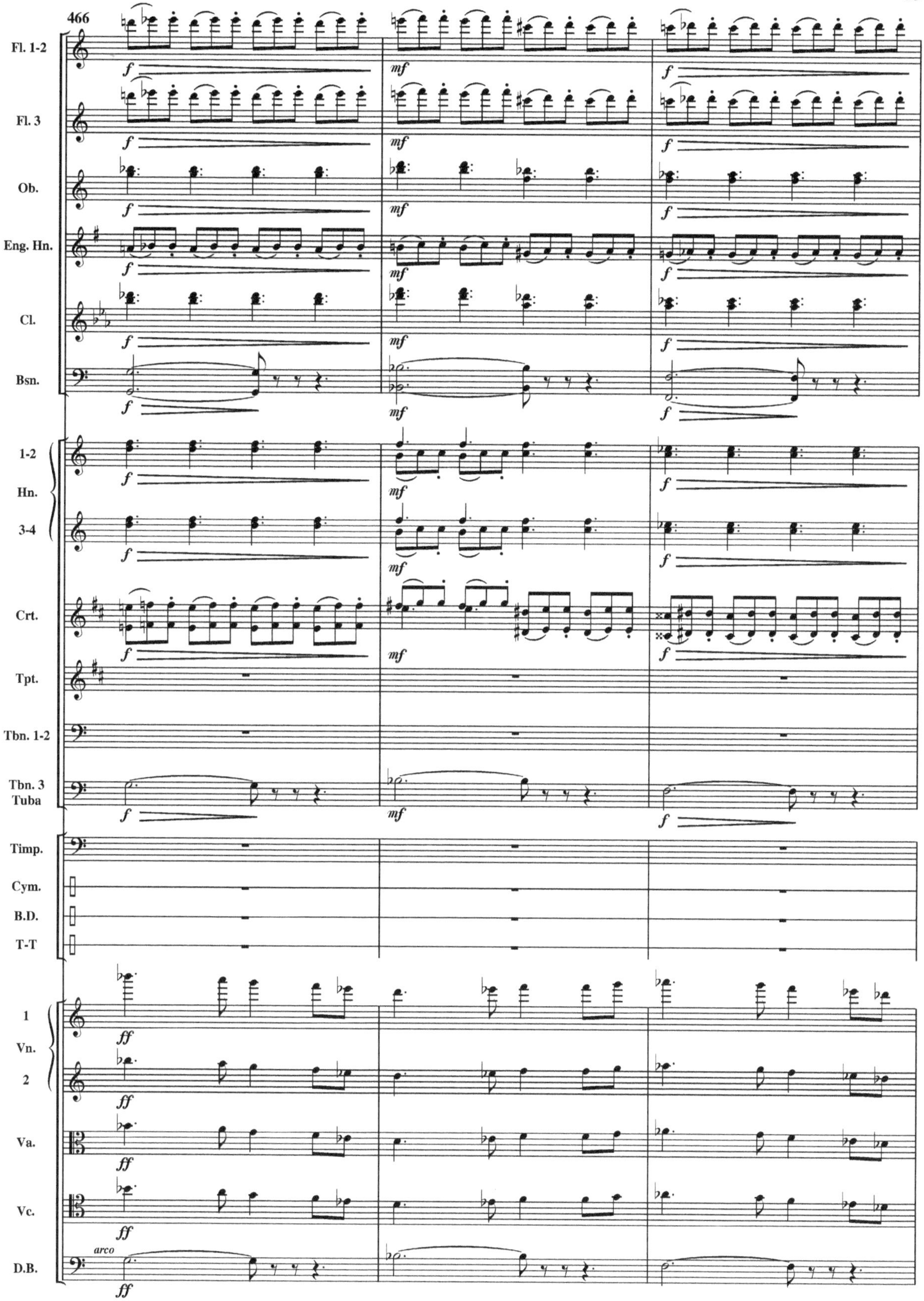
466
Fl. 1-2
Fl. 3
Ob.
Eng. Hn.
Cl.
Bsn.
1-2
Hn.
3-4
Crt.
Tpt.
Tbn. 1-2
Tbn. 3
Tuba
Timp.
Cym.
B.D.
T-T
1
Vn.
2
Va.
Vc.
arco
D.B.

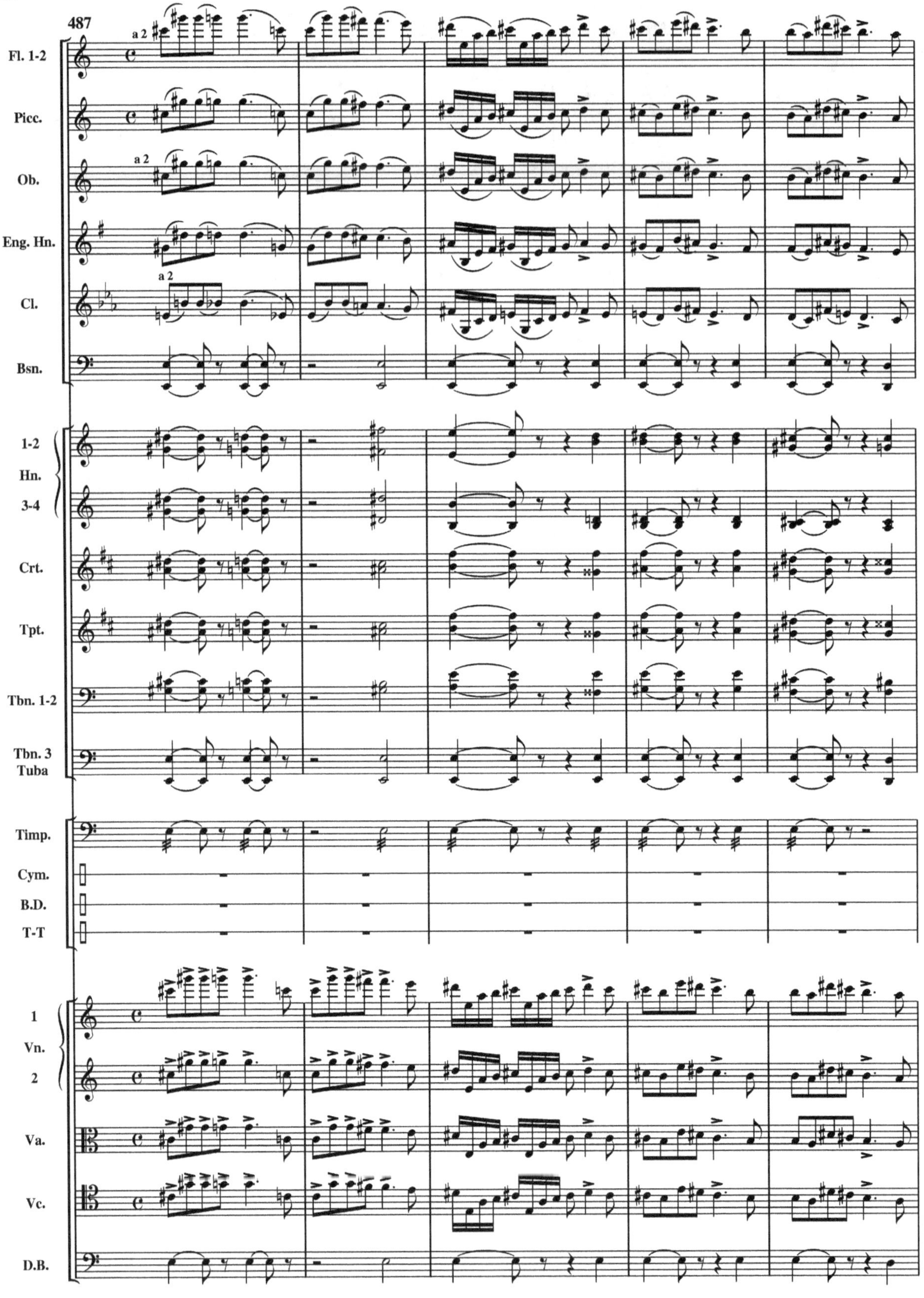
487
a 2
Fl. 1-2
Picc.
Ob.
Eng. Hn.
Cl.
Bsn.
1-2
Hn.
3-4
Crt.
Tpt.
Tbn. 1-2
Tbn. 3
Tuba
Timp.
Cym.
B.D.
T-T
1
Vn.
2
Va.
Vc.
D.B.

84

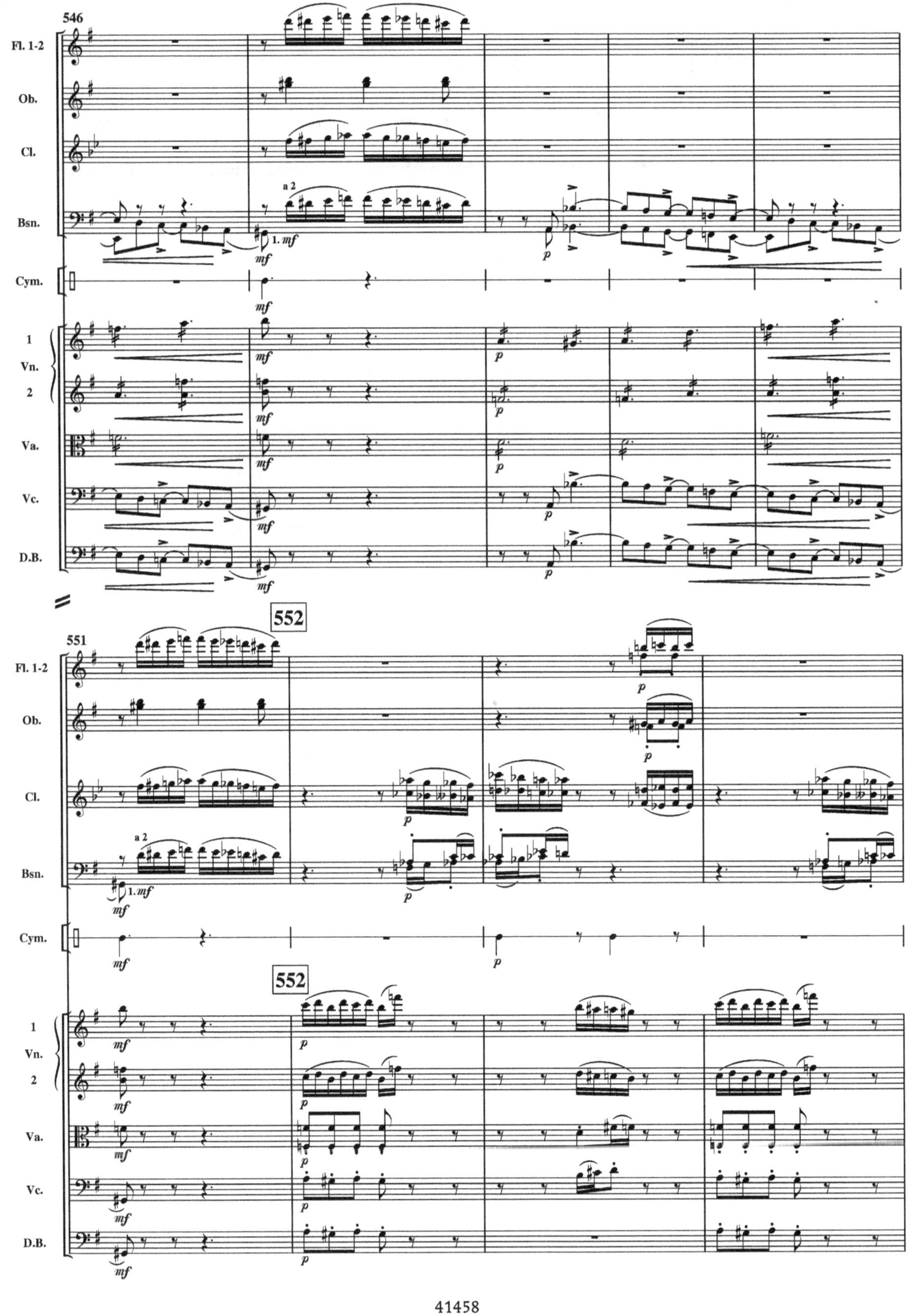
546
Fl. 1-2
Ob.
Cl.
Bsn.
a 2
1. mf
Cym.
Vn.
Va.
Vc.
D.B.
551
552

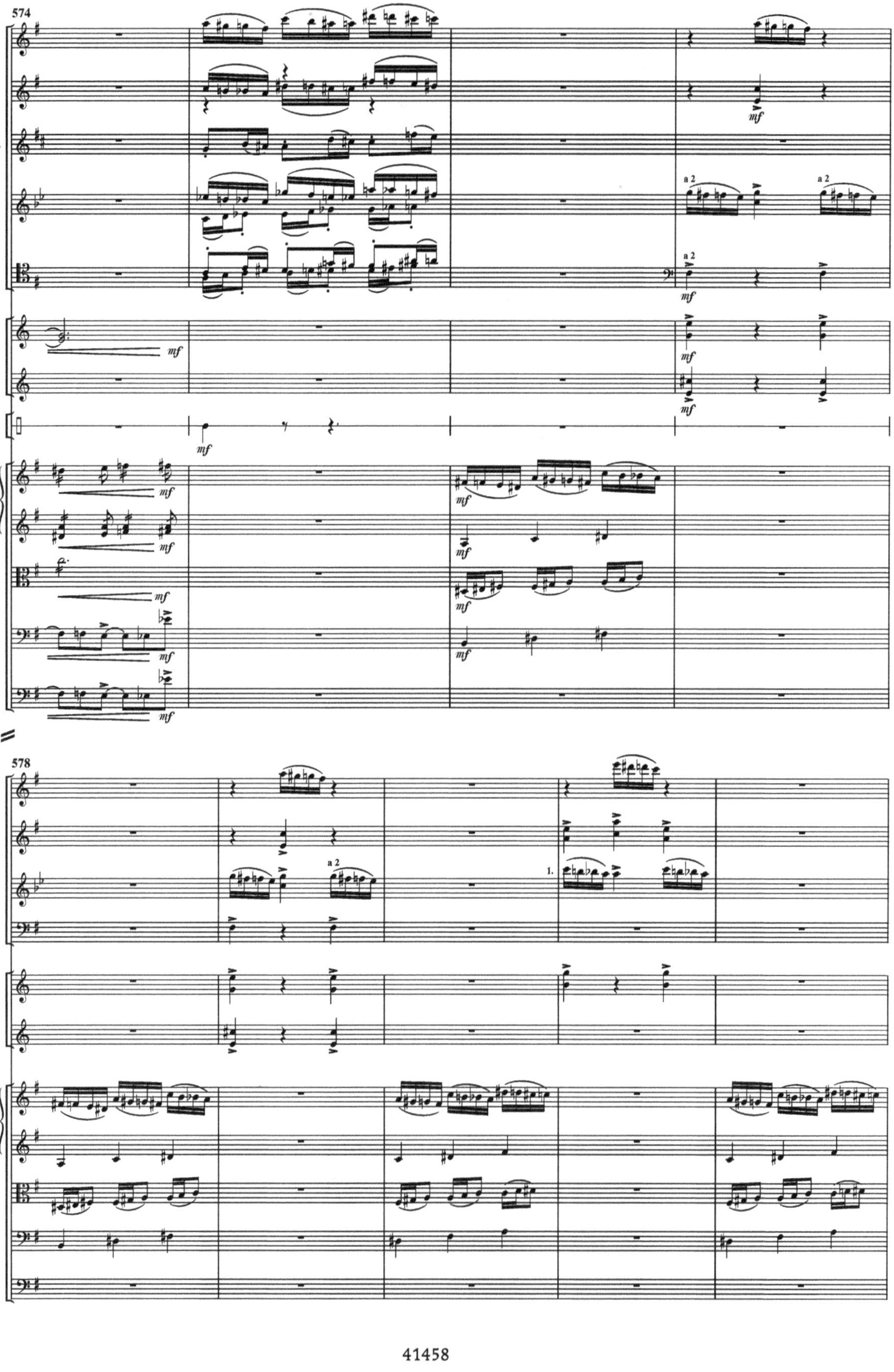
574
Fl. 1-2
Ob.
Eng. Hn.
Cl.
Bsn.
1-2
Hn.
3-4
Cym.
1
Vn.
2
Va.
Vc.
D.B.
a 2
mf
578
1.

94

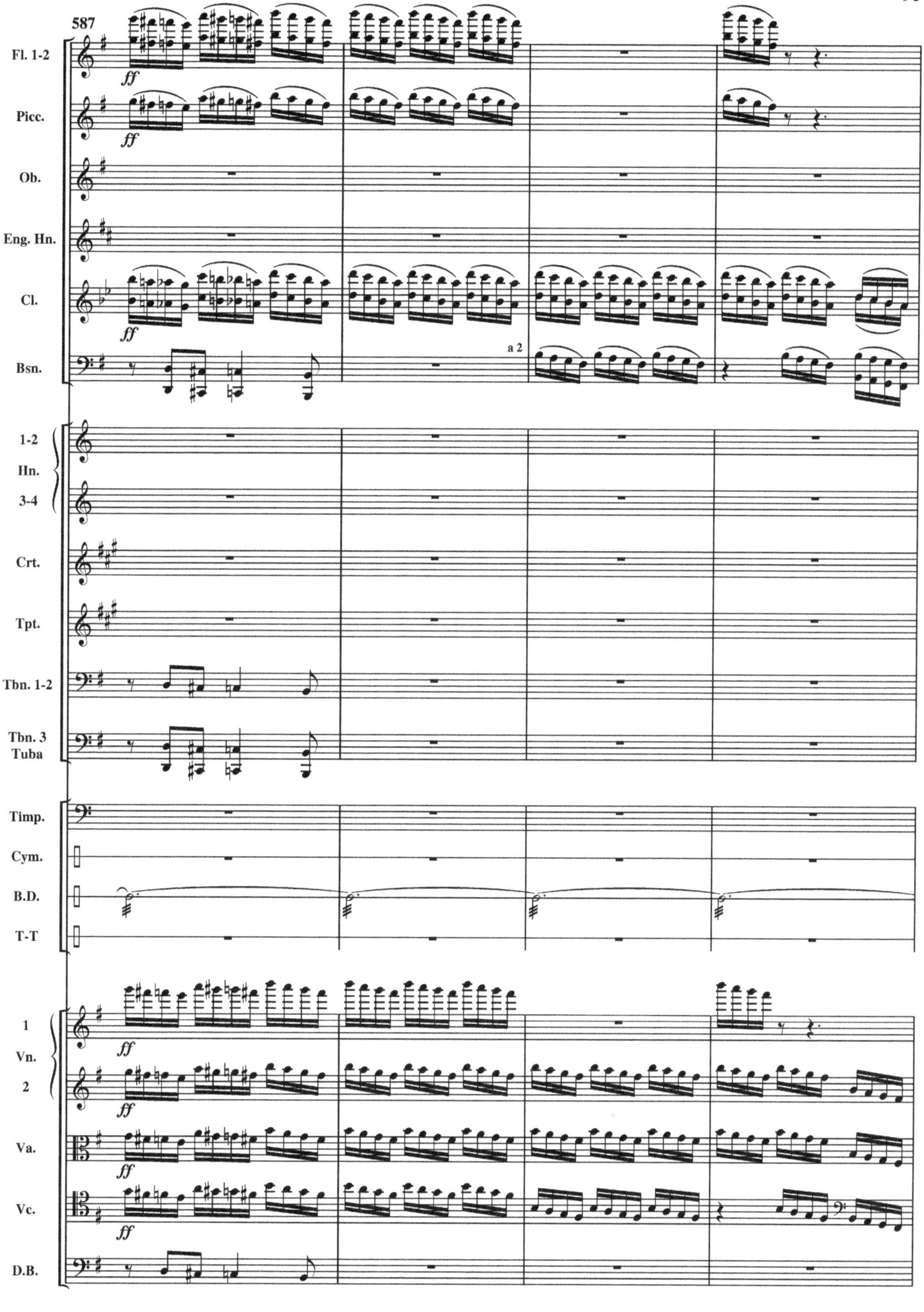
587
Fl. 1-2
Picc.
Ob.
Eng. Hn.
Cl.
Bsn.
a 2
1-2
Hn.
3-4
Crt.
Tpt.
Tbn. 1-2
Tbn. 3
Tuba
Timp.
Cym.
B.D.
T-T
1
Vn.
2
Va.
Vc.
D.B.
ff

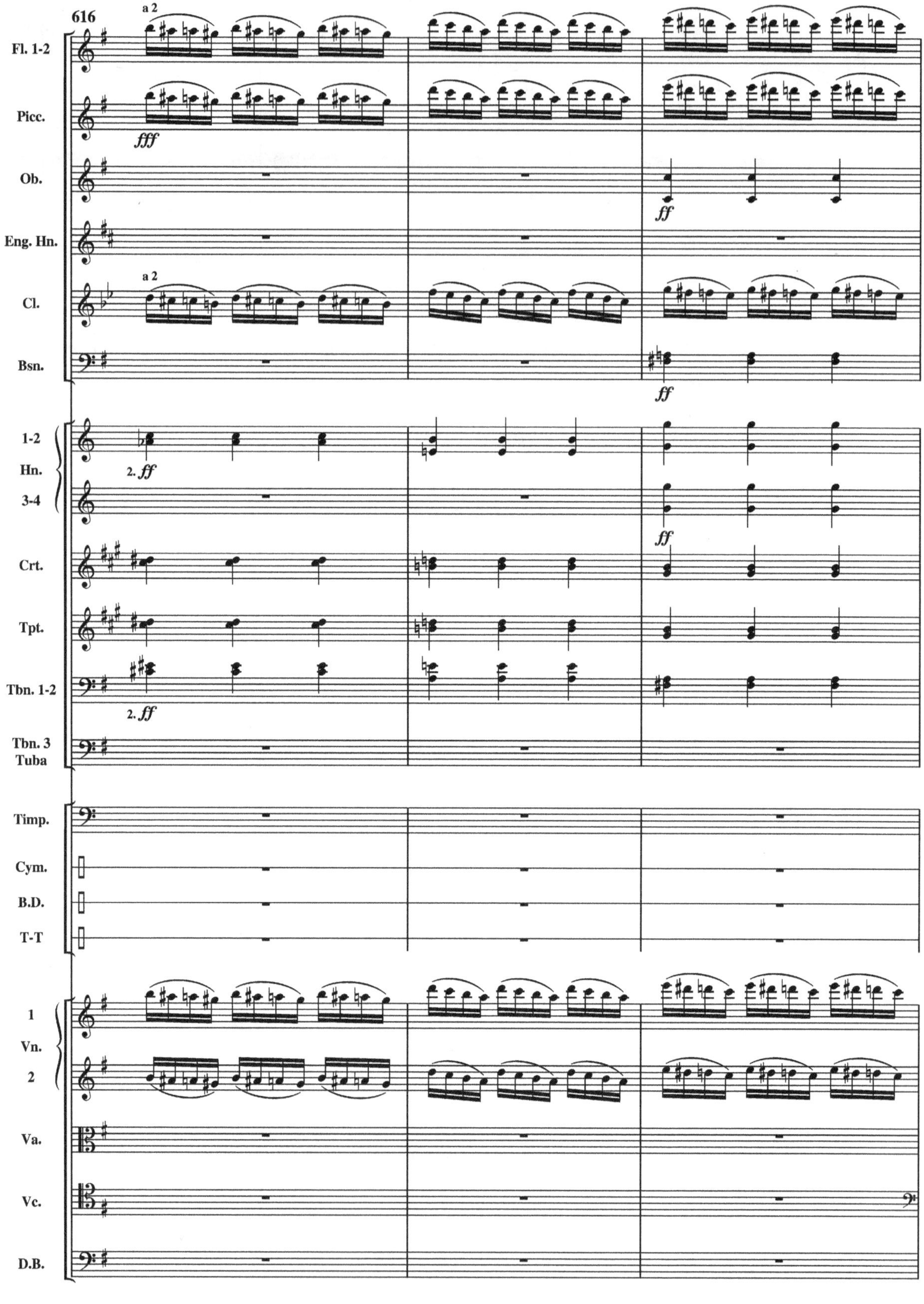
616
a 2
Fl. 1-2
Picc.
fff
Ob.
ff
Eng. Hn.
a 2
Cl.
Bsn.
ff
1-2
Hn.
3-4
2. ff
ff
Crt.
Tpt.
Tbn. 1-2
2. ff
Tbn. 3
Tuba
Timp.
Cym.
B.D.
T-T
1
Vn.
2
Va.
Vc.
D.B.

110

112

116

www.ingramcontent.com/pod-product-compliance
Lightning Source LLC
Chambersburg PA
CBHW080518110426
42742CB00017B/3154